CAUGHT IN THE HEART OF A NUCLEAR EXPLOSION, VICTIM OF GAMMA RADIATION GONE WILD, DOC NOW FINDS HIMSELF TRANSFORMED IN TIMES OF STRESS INTO THE DARK PERSONIFICATION OF HIS THE MOST POWERFUL MAN-LIKE CREATURE EVER TO WALK THE EARTH! ST

THE INCREDIBLE H

BASIC INSTINCT

HE COMES HERE TO BROOD.

TO THINK ABOUT HIS PLACE UNDER THE STARS.

Paul Jenkins
Writer
Mark Texiera
with
Richard Clark
Artists
Tom Smith
Colorist
John E. Workman
Letterer
Tom Brevoort
Editor
Bob Harras
Editor In Chief

THIS IS WHERE THE HULK WAS **BORN**, THIS OLD, ABANDONED TEST SITE AT THE EDGE OF THE DESERT.

THE WIND HERE SINGS ONLY TO **HIM**; SOFTLY ACROSS THE BAKED SAND, AS A MOTHER WOULD TO A CHILD. IT WHISPERS LONG-FORGOTTEN **SECRETS.**

HULK IS DRAWN TO THE SONG-- THIS IS WHERE HE COMES TO LISTEN TO THE ECHOES OF HIS OWN **CREATION.**

AND SOMETIMES THE SOUND HE IMAGINES HE HEARS IS THE VOICE OF HIS DISTANT INNER SELF, TAUNTING...

"YOUR MOMMY WAS A WASTELAND.

"YOUR DADDY DISAPPEARED IN A **FLASH.**"

HULK REMEMBERS WHEN HE CAME INTO THE WORLD. HIS BIRTH WAS QUITE *UNREMARKABLE*-- MUCHLIKE ANY OTHER BIRTH, WHEN IT COMES DOWN TO IT.

THERE WAS A LOT OF *PAIN.*

WHEN THE SCREAMING SUBSIDED, THE NEWBORN CREATURE WHO EMERGED MEWLING AND TERRIFIED FROM THE FUSION OF GAMMA RADIATION AND HUMAN ENDEAVOR TOOK ITS FIRST HESITANT STEPS.

THE HULK LOOKED AT THE WORLD AND BLINKED, THE WORLD LOOKED BACK IN *SILENCE.*

AND THERE, THE PAIN *REALLY* BEGAN.

5

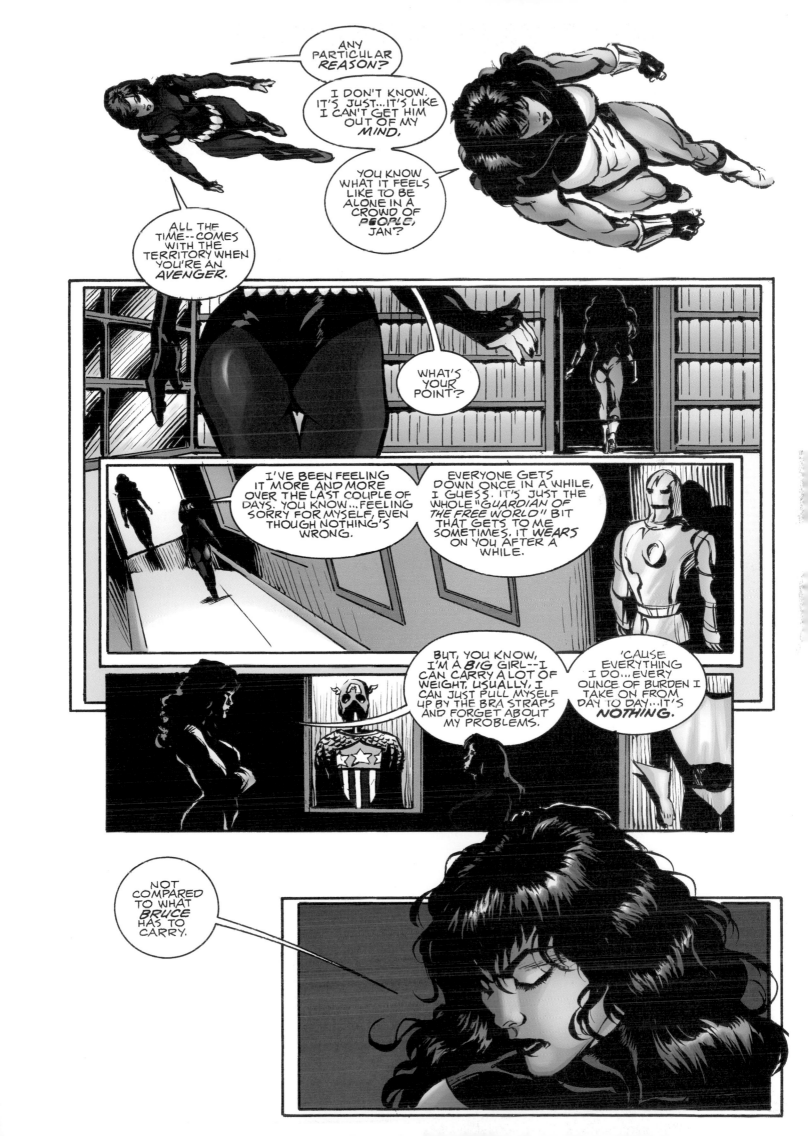

15

THERE IS AN IMPERCEPTIBLE SHIFT IN EXISTENCE AS REALITY CAVES INWARDS AND HULK IS BATHED IN THE MAGIC OF CHAOS. IT WASHES OVER AND THROUGH HIM.

HE HEARS HER THEN-- A DISTANT RIPPLE OF LAUGHTER...BUTTERFLY-SAD, LIKE WIND OVER THE COLD, HARD SAND. SHE IS A LONG-AGO WISH FOR HAPPINESS, FOR CLARITY.

HE WORRIES THAT HE CANNOT REMEMBER HER NAME, JUST AS THE LAUGHTER BEGINS TO FADE. AS IT GOES INTO NOTHINGNESS, SO DOES HIS FURY.

THEN THE BRUTE
IS AT PEACE FOR
A MOMENT...

27

I *DO* FIND IT SUSPICIOUS, THOUGH, THAT THE HULK JUST *HAPPENED* TO BE TEARING UP THE ALMA MATER OF HIS *ALTER EGO*--

--DOCTOR ROBERT BRUCE BANNER!

BANNER MUST'VE COME HERE SEEKING HELP TO FIND A *CURE!*

WELL, IT LOOKS LIKE HE STILL HASN'T FOUND ONE!

LORD, WHAT A *MESS...!*

I WAS HOPING FOR THE CHANCE TO USE THE *CRYO-INDUCER* PROTOTYPE ON HIM, SEE IF IT LIVES UP TO ITS *PROMISE*--

--OF PUTTING HIM INTO A STATE OF *SUSPENDED ANIMATION!**

BUT WE NEED TO KNOW WHERE THE BLAZES HE *IS*, FIRST!

* *INTRODUCED LAST ISSUE, FOR YOU LATECOMERS—JAUNTY JAYE.*

HE'S PROBABLY TURNED BACK INTO BANNER.

AFTER ALL, IT'S A *LOT* EASIER TO FIND A SEVEN-FOOT-TALL, RAMPAGING GREEN MONSTER...

"...THAN A SEEMINGLY NORMAL, MILD-MANNERED *HUMAN BEING.*"

BAD ENOUGH I'M RUNNING AROUND *HALF-NAKED*, BUT TO BE DOING IT IN THE *DESERT*, BEFORE THE SUN HAS FULLY RISEN--!

LUCKY I MADE IT BACK HERE TO *NAVAPO* BEFORE I SHIVERED MYSELF INTO *JELLY!*

NOW ALL I HAVE TO DO IS FIND *GEOFFREY CRAWFORD!*

STILL CAN'T BELIEVE HE ACTUALLY TRIED TO CURE HIMSELF OF A CRIPPLING *DISEASE--*

"--BY USING THE *MATTER-TELEPORTATION DEVICE* HE CREATED TO ALTER HIS DNA--"

"--SO THAT IT WOULD MATCH *MINE!*"

"HE THOUGHT HE'D GAIN THE HULK'S *HEALING FACTOR* AND *IMMUNE SYSTEM*..."

"...BUT INSTEAD HE BECAME A *MONSTER* LIKE THE HULK-- MAYBE *WORSE!*"

"DON'T REMEMBER MOST OF IT, BUT I KNOW HE WAS *STRONG*--AND *CLEVER!*"

"ENOUGH TO TAKE ON THE HULK--"

--AND, APPARENTLY, TO BREAK HIS *NECK!*

43

IF NOT FOR THE HULK'S HEALING FACTOR, I'D *SURELY* BE PARALYZED NOW-- OR *DEAD!*

AS IT IS, I *STILL* FEEL LIKE A TANK ROLLED OVER THE BACK OF MY HEAD!

CRAWFORD'S HOUSE IS JUST UP AHEAD AND--WAIT A MINUTE--

CRAWFORD--?

uhnn...

BRUCE... HELP ME...

...CAN'T... WALK... AGAIN...

EASY, PROFESSOR, I'VE GOT YOU!

LORD, HE'S *SO* FRAIL...!

SOON...

...I BEGAN TO FEEL *WEAK*, AND HAVE TROUBLE WITH MY *LEGS*, WHEN I SAW THE FIRST RAYS OF THE *SUN.*

I WAS CHANGING BACK TO *HUMAN* FORM, SO I TRIED TO MAKE IT BACK HERE BEFORE I WAS *PARALYZED* AGAIN.

hmh. I HAVE A *THEORY.* I ORIGINALLY CHANGED TO THE HULK AT *SUNSET,* AND BACK TO MYSELF AT *SUNRISE.*

YOU SEEM TO BE FOLLOWING THE SAME SCENARIO, AT LEAST FOR *NOW.*

THAT GIVES US A VERY *LIMITED* AMOUNT OF TIME TO STUDY YOUR CONDITION, BEFORE YOU CHANGE *AGAIN.*

WHAT DO YOU REMEMBER FROM LAST NIGHT?

EVERYTHING!

IT WAS AS IF I WAS SEEING THE WORLD THROUGH SOMEONE *ELSE'S* EYES.

SOMEONE *POWERFUL!* *FREE!*

AND YET-- STILL *ME*. IT WAS AN INCREDIBLE *RUSH!*

INTERESTING. I USUALLY DON'T REMEMBER MUCH FROM MY PERIODS AS THE HULK.

AND THE HULK ISN'T EVEN AWARE THAT HE AND I ARE ONE AND THE SAME.

THE STRENGTH COURSING THROUGH THESE VEINS, THE POWER IN THESE HANDS...

OUR MAIN CONCERN IS THAT YOU'LL BECOME THIS-- *RAVAGE* CREATURE-- ONCE AGAIN AT SUNSET.

BEFORE THAT CAN HAPPEN, WE HAVE TO QUICKLY FIND A WAY TO RESTORE YOU TO YOUR *ORIGINAL* CONDITION.

WHAT?! ARE YOU *INSANE?!*

I'M NOT GOING BACK TO BEING A DYING *INVALID!*

THERE *HAS* TO BE ANOTHER WAY!

WE NOW HAVE *PROOF* THAT I DON'T HAVE TO SPEND THE REST OF MY LIFE IN A *WHEELCHAIR!*

IF I EXPERIMENT *FURTHER*, I CAN *CORRECT* THIS CURRENT CONDITION AND--

NO!

YOUR *FIRST* ATTEMPT TURNED YOU INTO A VERY *DANGEROUS* CREATURE WHO SEEMS TO GET OFF ON THE POWER HE POSSESSES--

--A CREATURE WHO PROUDLY CALLS HIMSELF "RAVAGE"!

YOU HAVE TO SUBMIT TO A *REVERSAL* OF THE PROCESS--

KNOCK

KNOCK

KNOCK

WH--WHO IS IT?

ANY *FURTHER* ATTEMPTS COULD MAKE THINGS *WORSE!*

THIS IS GENERAL THADDEUS ROSS AND MAJOR GLENN TALBOT--

--FROM *GAMMA BASE!*

OH, NO!

THEY'RE LOOKING FOR ME!

HIDE DOWN IN THE *BASEMENT*. I WON'T LET ON THAT YOU'RE HERE.

THANK YOU, PROFESSOR!

IT'S *UNLOCKED*, COME ON IN....!

SEVERAL MINUTES LATER...

...WE'VE DETERMINED THAT THE *ORIGIN POINT* OF LAST NIGHT'S HULK RAMPAGE WAS *YOUR* LAB, ON THE D.S.U. CAMPUS.

REALLY? THAT'S-- SHOCKING!

PROFESSOR, HAVE YOU HAD ANY CONTACT AT ALL WITH BRUCE BANNER?

DO YOU KNOW HIS WHERE-ABOUTS?

uh...

hmh. HE SAID HE'S ALL *ALONE* HERE.

SO WHY IS HIS WHEELCHAIR SO FAR *AWAY* FROM HIM?

WHY WOULD HE MAKE IT *HARDER* FOR HIMSELF TO GET AROUND?

GENTLEMEN... THERE'S SOMETHING YOU SHOULD KNOW...

AND...

FREEZE, BANNER!

WHAT--?

CRAWFORD BETRAYED ME!

QUICK, GLENN-- *SHOOT!*

ATTABOY!

FFFT

TRANQUILIZER DART?! WAIT! YOU DON'T UNDERSTAND--!

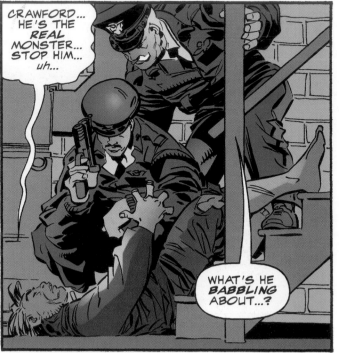

CRAWFORD... HE'S THE *REAL* MONSTER... STOP HIM... *uh*...

WHAT'S HE *BABBLING* ABOUT...?

SHORTLY...

PUT HIM IN THE *VAULT-TRUCK!* AND MAKE SURE HE *DOESN'T* REGAIN CONSCIOUSNESS.

THANKS FOR YOUR *COOPERATION*, PROFESSOR! SORRY ABOUT ALL THE *TROUBLE!*

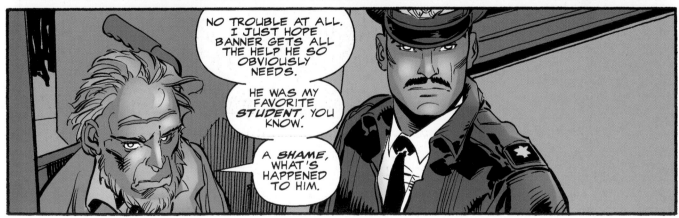

NO TROUBLE AT ALL. I JUST HOPE BANNER GETS ALL THE HELP HE SO OBVIOUSLY NEEDS.

HE WAS MY FAVORITE *STUDENT*, YOU KNOW.

A *SHAME*, WHAT'S HAPPENED TO HIM.

NOW THAT MY HAPLESS FORMER PUPIL IS OUT OF THE WAY--

--I CAN GET BACK TO WORK!

I AM *NEVER* GOING BACK TO BEING WHAT I *WAS!*

EVEN IF I HAVE TO SETTLE FOR BEING WHOLE AGAIN FROM SUNSET TO SUNRISE, I'LL *TAKE* IT--AT LEAST FOR *NOW!*

BUT THERE'S *GOT* TO BE A WAY FOR ME TO HAVE THE STRENGTH-- THE POWER-- *ALL* THE TIME!

AND I'LL FIND IT! NO ONE WILL STOP ME!

"NOT EVEN THE HULK!"

GAMMA BASE, DEDICATED TO THE CAPTURE AND NEUTRALIZATION OF THE RAMPAGING HULK.

SEVERAL HOURS LATER.

IN A SPECIALLY-DESIGNED VAULT BUILT TO WITHSTAND THE RAW POWER OF THE GAMMA-SPAWNED CREATURE...

...HIS ALL-TOO-HUMAN ALTER-EGO FINDS HIMSELF WITH A VISITOR.

ⵀⵀⵀⵀ... GO...'WAY, BETTY...

JUST... LEAVE ME... ALONE.

STOP IT, BRUCE. I *CARE* ABOUT YOU. EVEN IF YOU AND I AREN'T *TOGETHER* ANYMORE...

...I *STILL* CARE.

DON'T... DON'T *BOTHER*...

...LIKE YOU SAID...WE'RE NOT TOGETHER...ANYMORE.

NOT...I'M NOT...YOUR *BURDEN*... ANY LONGER.

YOU WERE *NEVER* A BURDEN TO ME, BRUCE! I *LOVED* YOU!

AND YET...YOU MARRIED *TALBOT*...THE ONE YOUR *FATHER*... ACTUALLY *APPROVED* OF...

GO HOME, BETTY...BACK TO YOUR *HUSBAND*... WHERE YOU *BELONG*.

IT'S BEST...FOR *BOTH* OF US.

BRUCE...

VERY SLEEPY...PUMPED FULL OF SEDATIVES... TO KEEP ME FROM CHANGING...

...SLEEPY...

...JUST GO.

OUTSIDE...

...BETTY, ARE YOU ALL RIGHT?

I'M *FINE*, GLENN. IT'S *NOTHING*.

GLENN...IS THERE ANY CHANCE WE CAN GO *AWAY* FOR A WHILE? TAKE A VACATION?

I'M STARTING TO FEEL VERY... *CONFINED* HERE.

MAYBE YOU CAN PUT IN FOR SOME *LEAVE* TIME--YOU'VE CERTAINLY *EARNED* IT.

I'LL TRY. WITH BANNER CAPTURED NOW, IT'S DEFINITELY A POSSIBILITY.

THANK YOU, LOVE. I'M *ALREADY* RELIEVED!

AND IF WE *DO* MANAGE TO GET AWAY FROM HERE, MY DARLING--WILL YOU BE RUNNING AWAY WITH *ME*--

--OR AWAY FROM *BANNER*?

THAT EVENING...

...BLAST IT, WAKE UP!

WAKE UP, BANNER...

HUH? WHERE...?

ROSS...?

WE'VE JUST RECEIVED A REPORT FROM NAVADO--

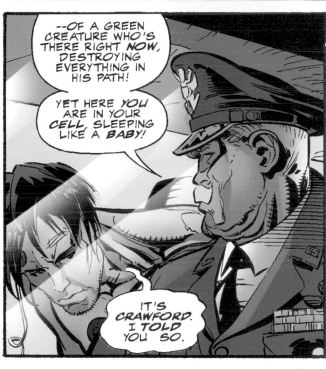

--OF A GREEN CREATURE WHO'S THERE RIGHT *NOW*, DESTROYING EVERYTHING IN HIS PATH!

YET HERE *YOU* ARE IN YOUR *CELL*, SLEEPING LIKE A *BABY*!

IT'S *CRAWFORD*. I *TOLD* YOU SO.

NEVER MIND "I TOLD YOU SO"! I'VE ALREADY SENT TALBOT AND THE *HULKBUSTERS* OUT TO *FACE* THIS CREATURE--

--BUT WE NEED TO KNOW MORE *ABOUT* HIM! WHAT CAN YOU TELL ME?

SO NOW YOU WANT MY *HELP*? AFTER LOCKING ME UP LIKE I'M SOME KIND OF *ANIMAL*?

BLAST YOU, BANNER! THERE ARE HUMAN LIVES AT STAKE!

I KNOW. WHICH IS WHY I *WILL* HELP YOU, ROSS.

BUT YOU'VE GOT TO TAKE ME *TO* HIM!

I'M THE ONLY ONE WHO CAN RETURN HIM TO *NORMAL*!

I KNOW I'M GONNA REGRET THIS...!

THE TOWN OF NAVAPO...

THAT'S IT! RUN! RUN AWAY!

HA HA HA HA!

MY GOD

A MONSTER

IS IT THE HULK?

INSANE

YOU'RE ALL *PATHETIC!* HELPLESS AND *WEAK!* JUST AS I WAS, A SHORT TIME AGO!

SWISSHH

BUT LOOK AT ME *NOW!*

PA.

KRAKSH

YOU ALL *PITIED* THE SICK LITTLE *INVALID,* DIDN'T YOU?

NOW YOU CAN *FEAR* HIM!

FWA

BOOM

uhn! EXPLOSIVE SHELL--? WHO WOULD *DARE* TO SHOOT AT ME?

AND SO WOEFULLY *UNPREPARED!*

YOU DON'T STAND A *CHANCE* AGAINST ME!

HA HA HA HA!

AH, OUR EVER-VIGILANT *ARMED FORCES!*

SO BRAVE! SO WELL-EQUIPPED!

JUST AS WE *THOUGHT*-- IT'S *NOT* THE HULK!

SO NOW WE HAVE YET *ANOTHER* MONSTER ON OUR HANDS!

"FIRE!"

VHOOOOSH

FWA-TOOOM

HA HA HA

HA HA HA!

OH MY GOD!

YOU WANT TO SEE *POWER?*

I'LL SHOW YOU *POWER!*

DEAR LORD, NO!

WHA-BOOOM!

GET THE HINT?

TARGET HIM WITH THE *CRYO-INDUCER!*

TRYING, SIR--

"--BUT HE'S LEAPING AWAY!"

HA HA HA HA

KEEP HIM IN SIGHT-- MAINTAIN PURSUIT!

THE CAMPUS OF DESERT STATE UNIVERSITY.

PHYSICS

MATTER TRANSPORTATION PODS?!

WE *WONDERED* WHAT THESE THINGS WERE WHEN WE INSPECTED THIS LAB EARLIER, BUT I NEVER WOULDA *DREAMED*--!

THIS WAS CRAWFORD'S PET PROJECT FOR *YEARS*--

--AND IT'S WHAT TURNED HIM INTO THAT *CREATURE*-- RAVAGE!

I'VE RETRIEVED ALL THE NECESSARY COMPUTER FLOPPY DISKS CONTAINING ALL THE PERTINENT DATA...

...I FIGURE I CAN *REPLACE* THE WRECKED COMPUTER AND *REPROGRAM* IT--

--TO RESTORE CRAWFORD'S DNA TO ITS *ORIGINAL* CONFIGURATION.

WE NEED TO WAIT UNTIL HE CHANGES BACK INTO *HUMAN* FORM, WHEN HE'S *VULNERABLE*--

--AND *FORCE* HIM INTO THE PODS!

SAME STRATEGY YOU USE WITH *ME*, GENERAL.

HAVE TO USE THESE PODS ON *MYSELF* AS WELL--

--THEY MAY BE MY ONLY CHANCE FOR A FINAL *CURE*!

WHAT THE--?

I *THOUGHT* I SPOTTED INTRUDERS IN MY LAB!

THWA- BOOOM

LUCKY FOR ME I WAS PASSING BY, AS I SPREAD THE WORD ABOUT MY *ARRIVAL*!

UNLUCKY FOR *YOU*, THOUGH!

GET *BACK*, GENERAL!

BANNER-- IS THAT-- *CRAWFORD*?!

WAS CRAWFORD ROSS! NOW YOU CAN CALL ME-- *RAVAGE*!

AND *YOU*, BANNER--NO DOUBT YOU'RE HERE TO TURN MY OWN DEVICE *AGAINST* ME!

WELL, THAT CAN'T HAPPEN--

--IF THE DEVICE NO LONGER *EXISTS*!

KRUNCH

CRAWFORD, *NO*!

YOU'RE DESTROYING *BOTH* OUR CHANCES!

NO CURE FOR *ME*-- AND YOU'LL *REMAIN* A NIGHT-STALKING *MONSTER*!

AND YOU'LL *STILL* BECOME PARALYZED AND SICK AGAIN AT *SUNRISE*!

WRONG, BANNER! I'VE MADE *OTHER* ARRANGEMENTS!

I STILL HAVE MY *PROTOTYPE PODS*-- NOW HIDDEN AWAY! *YOU'LL* NEVER FIND THEM--BUT I'VE ALREADY USED THEM TO KEEP ME IN THIS FORM *PERMANENTLY*!

OH, GOOD LORD IN HEAVEN--

--I KNEW I WAS GONNA REGRET THIS!

EXCELLENT! NOW I CAN FINISH YOU OFF--

--ONCE AND FOR ALL!

NEVER! HULK REMEMBERS WHAT YOU DID, RAVAGE!

WHAM

URK--!

YOU TRIED TO BREAK HULK'S NECK!

HULK OWES YOU FOR THAT!

POOM

AAAGH!

YOU SEE, RAVAGE? THE MADDER HULK GETS, THE STRONGER HULK GETS!

SO HULK WILL GET MADDER AND MADDER AT YOU, RAVAGE--

--AND HULK WILL GET STRONGER AND STRONGER--

--AND THEN HULK WILL SMASH YOU TO BITS!

BAMP

KRAKSH

IT'S CALLED "STRAGEDY"!

THWUMP

RAARRGH!

THIS-- ISN'T AS EASY--AS I *THOUGHT* IT WOULD BE!

HE'S SO *WILD*--SO *PRIMAL*!

HAVEN'T SEEN ANYTHING LIKE THIS SINCE THE *ABOMINATION* FIRST SHOWED UP!

WASN'T QUITE SURE WHO TO ROOT FOR BACK *THEN*, EITHER!

UNGHN!

WAP

CAN BARELY-- PUT UP A *DEFENSE*!

RRMMMMMBLLE

PA-KRAK

UH-OH-- THIS PLACE IS COMIN' APART AT THE *SEAMS*!

MAYBE THESE TWO GORILLAS CAN SURVIVE WHEN THE WALLS COME TUMBLIN' DOWN--

--SMASH YOU--

‹URK›

--BUT THIS OLD SOLDIER DEFINITELY *WOULDN'T*!

GOTTA GET *OUT* OF HERE-- *PRONTO*!

KRA-POKK

THERE HE IS--

--FIRE!

WHA--

SHHAK

IT *WORKED!* THE CRYO-INDUCER WORKED!

LOOKS LIKE WE GOT HERE JUST IN *TIME!*

GENERAL--YOU'RE IN THE LINE OF FIRE!

GET OUT OF THE WAY--

--SO WE CAN FREEZE THE *HULK,* TOO!

GENERAL--?!